Spot the Shape

Shapes in Buildings

Rebecca Rissman

www.raintreepublishers.co.uk
Visit our website to find out more information about Raintree books.

To order:

Phone 0845 6044371
Fax +44 (0) 1865 312263
Email myorders@capstonepub.co.uk

Customers from outside the UK please telephone +44 1865 312262

Raintree is an imprint of Capstone Global Library Limited, a company incorporated in England and Wales having its registered office at 7 Pilgrim Street, London, EC4V 6LB – Registered company number: 6695582

First published in hardback in 2009
Paperback edition first published in 2010

Edited by Rebecca Rissman, Charlotte Guillain and Catherine Veitch
Designed by Joanna Hinton-Malivoire
Picture research by Tracy Cummins and Heather Mauldin
Originated by Dot Gradations Ltd
Printed in China by South China Printing Company Ltd

ISBN 978 0431 19289 5 (hardback)
13 12 11 10 09
10 9 8 7 6 5 4 3 2 1

ISBN 978 0431 19295 6 (paperback)
14 13 12 11 10
10 9 8 7 6 5 4 3 2 1

British Library Cataloguing in Publication Data
Rissman, Rebecca
Shapes in buildings. - (Acorn. Spot the shape)
516.1'5
A full catalogue record for this book is available from the British Library.

Acknowledgements
We would like to thank the following for permission to reproduce photographs: ©Age Fotostock pp. **17** (Philip Bier), **18** (Philip Bier); ©Alamy pp. **9** (Robert Harding Picture Library Ltd/Marco Simoni), **10** (Robert Harding Picture Library Ltd/Marco Simoni), **11** (Rainer Jahns), **12** (Rainer Jahns); ©Getty Images pp. **4** (Superstudio), **7** (Keren Su), **8** (Keren Su), **21** (Alan Copson); ©REUTERS pp. **15** (Euroluftbild.de), **16** (Euroluftbild.de), **23b** (Euroluftbild.de); ©Shutterstock pp. **6** (Claudio Zaccherini), **19** (Dainis Derics), **20** (Dainis Derics), **23a** (Dainis Derics); ©Viesti Associates pp. **13** (Ken Ross), **14** (Ken Ross).

Cover photograph of Louvre Museum, Paris reproduced with permission of ©SuperStock/age fotostock. Back cover photograph of a domed building in Cadiz, Spain reproduced with permission of ©Shutterstock (Dainis Derics).

Every effort has been made to contact copyright holders of material reproduced in this book. Any omissions will be rectified in subsequent printings if notice is given to the publishers.

Contents

Shapes

There are shapes all around us.

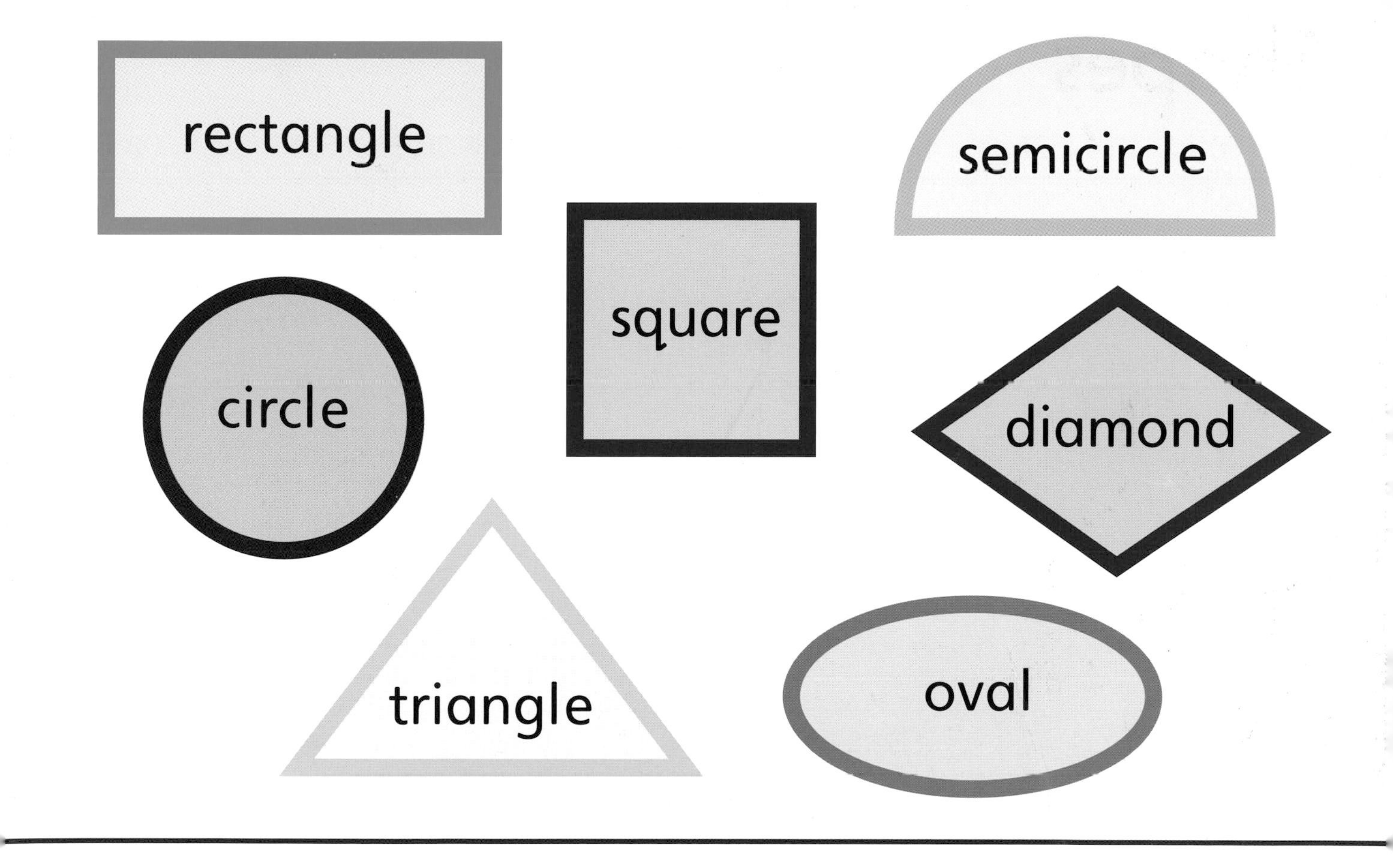

Each shape has a name.

Shapes in buildings

There are many shapes in buildings.

What shape is in this door?

There is a circle in this door.

What shapes are on this building?

This building has diamonds on it.

What shape is in the roofs on this building?

There are triangles in the roofs on this building.

What shape are these windows?

These windows are squares.

What shape can you see in this stadium?

There is an oval in this stadium.

What shape is this house?

This house is a rectangle.

What shape is the dome on this building?

The dome is a semicircle.

There are many shapes in buildings.
What shapes can you see?

Naming shapes

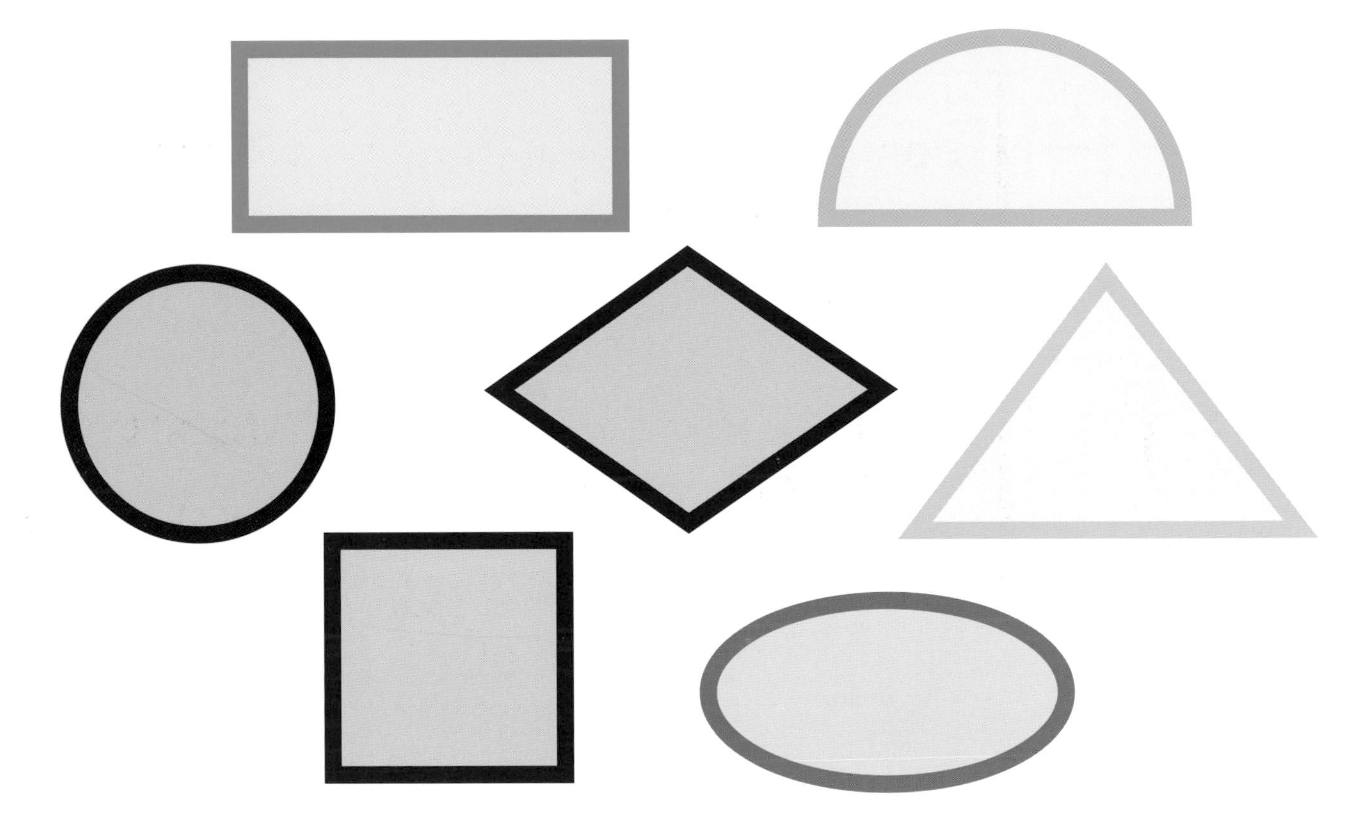

Can you remember the names of these shapes?

Picture glossary

dome roof of a building in the shape of the top half of a ball

stadium large sports ground with seats for people to sit on

Index

Notes for parents and teachers

Before reading

Make two sets of the shapes shown on page 22 out of card. Hold up each shape in turn to the class and ask the children what it is called. As you hold up each shape sing the following song to the tune of "If You're Happy and You Know It": "A circle is a shape that goes round (two times), A circle is a shape, That goes round and round and round, A circle is a shape that goes round." Adapt the song for each shape.

After reading

- Help the children to make a town skyline with silhouettes of different shapes such as domes, roofs, and skyscrapers. Label the buildings and display them on the classroom wall.
- Ask the children to make buildings with different shapes using construction bricks. Ask them to name the shapes they have used.